French Paintings and Drawings

A GIFT FROM OUR

SISTER CITY,

AIRDRIE IN THE

MONKLANDS,

SCOTLAND

Art Gallery & Museum Glasgow

French Paintings and Drawings

Illustrated summary catalogue

Art Gallery & Museum Glasgow

ILLUSTRATIONS
©ADAGP 1985

Pierre Bonnard	Edge of the forest
Georges Braque	Still life
Charles Camoin	Place de Clichy, Paris
André Derain	Blackfriars
Othon Friesz	The Seine at Paris – Pont de Grenelle
André Lhote	Negress
André Lhote	Nude
Albert Marquet	Algiers Harbour
Gregoire Michonze	Children at play
Lucien Simon	Staging post; After the war; Horses running free

©DACS 1985

Emile Bernard	Landscape St Briac
Raoul Dufy	The pier at Deauville
Henri Le Sidaner	Square in Beauvais, moonlight; Nemours
Maximilien Luce	Landscape with willow trees
Louis Marcoussis	Table on the balcony
Henri Matisse	Head of a young girl; The pink table-cloth
Pierre Montezin	The meadow in June
Pablo Picasso	The flower seller
Georges Rouault	Circus girl
Paul Signac	Coal crane, Clichy
Paul Signac	Sunset at Herblay
Maurice Utrillo	Village street, Auvers-sur-Oise
Maurice de Vlaminck	A woody river scene
Edouard Vuillard	The lady in green; The table; Interior of the drawing room; Lunch in the country; Mother and child

Published by Glasgow Museums and Art Galleries
©1985 Glasgow Museums and Art Galleries
ISBN 0 902752 24 3

Cover: Jules Adolphe Aimé Louis BRETON
1827-1906
The reapers (detail)

Text: Anne Donald
Photographs: Museums' Photographic Department
Design: Sandy Hamilton

Preface

This is the first publication to list and illustrate every French picture in Glagow Art Gallery's main collection at Kelvingrove.

For a variety of reasons the two previous French catalogues, published in 1967 and 1953, omitted a number of works, among them many of doubtful attribution. Since 1967 some problems have been solved although the authorship of several items remains uncertain. To assist scholars a numerical index and concordance, which contains cross-references to previous attributions, is given at the back of this publication, along with a subject index.

Most of the pictures are in oil but there is also a small group of watercolours, pastels and drawings. Prints, of which the gallery has over 800 French examples dating from the 16th to the 20th century, are not included here and neither are the works in the Burrell Collection which will be separately catalogued.

Glasgow Art Gallery's 19th and early 20th century French paintings are justly famous and it is hoped that this summary catalogue will be an attractive introduction to the collection.

Alasdair A Auld
Director

Contents

Vincent van GOGH 1853-1890
Portrait of Alexander Reid (1854-1928) 1887

Introduction

The history of Glasgow Art Gallery's French collection

Glasgow Art Gallery's collection was founded in 1854 with the bequest of Archibald McLellan,[1] a wealthy coachbuilder and a man of wide cultural and civic interests. He bequeathed to the city 510 oil paintings,[2] along with the buildings in which they were housed. Unfortunately he died insolvent and Glasgow Corporation had to be persuaded to buy the pictures and the galleries. Somewhat reluctantly they paid £15,000 for the paintings and £29,500 for the buildings but the purchase soon proved to be a shrewd one as the collection rapidly attracted further gifts and bequests. In 1902 the pictures moved to their new home at Kelvingrove which was built to coincide with the 1901 International Exhibition, but the McLellan Galleries still exist in Sauchiehall Street where their remaining connection with the art world is limited to housing occasional temporary exhibitions, in particular the annual shows of The Royal Glasgow Institute of the Fine Arts.

McLellan's collection consisted largely of Italian, Dutch and Flemish old masters many of which are of top quality, but few of his pictures were of French origin. Only 36 of the 427 items in the first published catalogue (1855) were listed as French – although to this number can be added seven more which were included under Italian or Flemish schools. It is now impossible to identify some of these 43 paintings partly because several sales from the collection were held later in the 19th century and partly because attributions and titles were changed frequently in the early years.[3] When the McLellan Collection was eventually entered in the Gallery's picture register the number of French paintings had been reduced to 19. Of these only 11 appear in the present volume, the remaining eight having been re-attributed to other schools, although to this group can now be added five more McLellan pictures originally registered as Flemish or Italian. A few of these 16 items are of top quality but others are only copies or pastiches. However the exceptions include one of the stars of the whole collection – *St Maurice (or St Victor) with a donor* originally attributed to the Flemish painter Mabuse but now accepted by all authorities as being by the late 15th century French artist known as The Master of Moulins. Two other McLellan pictures of note are *The Four Seasons,* recently attributed to Vouet, and the problematic 15th century Franco-Italian *Nativity.*

Glasgow's municipal collection of French paintings, now of international significance, did not therefore have a particularly promising start. Subsequent major 19th century gifts and bequests, which largely completed Glasgow's holdings of Dutch, Flemish and Italian old masters, also contained few French pictures of quality. For example the Euing Bequest of 1874[4] consisted of over 100 paintings, mostly Dutch and Flemish, but there were only seven French items, six of which have been identified as copies. With the equally large, though less important, bequest of Adam Teacher in 1898[5] came a small group of indifferent 19th century French anecdotal works. Even the fine collection of the portrait painter John Graham-Gilbert[6] included just two French pictures, one of which was later identified as Flemish, although the other, Gaspar Dughet's *Ideal Landscape,* is of real interest. It seems therefore that the early to mid 19th century Glaswegians whose collections eventually came to Kelvingrove had little interest in French art. The reasons for this have not been fully investigated but apart from Claude, Dughet and Poussin (who in any case were often categorised as Italian), French painting does not seem to have been generally fashionable in Britain at this time. In his letters and memoirs William Buchanan,[7] the early 19th century dealer and entrepreneur, wrote little about French pictures, and British auction sales[8] of the period listed remarkably few pre-19th century French works compared to the number of Italian, Dutch and Flemish old masters. Also it seems likely that even had such items been readily available much of the 17th and 18th century French baroque and rococo subject matter would have been considered too frivolous by Scots collectors.

Later in the 19th century however fashions changed and the next generation of local collectors started to buy contemporary French art, mostly by realist and Barbizon school painters. The first important 19th century French pictures to enter the Gallery's collection were presented in 1896 by the sons of James Reid of Auchterarder.[9] This gift included a large late work by Corot, *Pastorale – souvenir d'Italie,* which is said to have been one of the first two Corots to come to Scotland.[10] In 1901 the Gallery acquired the first of its seven paintings by Monticelli, an artist whose immense popularity with Scottish collectors was due initially to the Glasgow-born dealer and stained glass designer Daniel Cottier.[11]

The reasons for the later 19th century collectors' change in taste were partly that the subject matter of realist and Barbizon works appealed to them but also that such pictures were being popularised in Glasgow by a number of dealers. Foremost among these was Craibe Angus[12] who opened his gallery in the city in 1874 and was the first Scottish dealer to specialise in Hague and Barbizon school pictures. His influence is reflected at Kelvingrove, notably in the collection of one of his customers, James Donald,[13] who bequeathed 42 pictures to the Gallery in 1905.

The Donald Bequest contained the first large and important collection of French paintings acquired by Glasgow. Most of these 19 works are by artists associated with the Barbizon school, including Corot, Daubigny, Millet, Monticelli and Rousseau. The pictures are nearly all of good quality and two are outstanding – *Going to work* by J F Millet and *The sheepfold,* a pastel by the same artist. Donald's French collection was largely complete by 1888 when he lent many items to the International Exhibition which was held that year in Kelvingrove Park to raise funds to build the present Art Gallery and Museum. This bequest gave the city a good range of pre-Impressionist paintings which made an appropriate foundation for later acquisitions.

As the Gallery did not start purchasing until the 1890s and did not buy a French picture until 1913, the nature of the collection formed before then is entirely a reflection of the taste of its benefactors. As a result Glasgow's French collection, so rich in works from the mid 19th century onwards, lacks a good representation of earlier art and no serious attempt has ever been made to remedy this situation. The first French painting bought by the Corporation was however a wise choice. Bastien-Lepage's *Poor Fauvette* of 1881 was a significant acquisition not only because of the artist's importance as a French realist but also because of his influence on the early work of the Glasgow Boys.

There then followed a period of little growth in the expansion of the French collection with only a handful of lesser works being added.[14] (The first gift of French pictures from William Burrell came in 1925 but that collection was destined eventually to be separately administered and housed and is not included in the present publication.) It was not until 1929 that another important French painting came to the main collection. *Chrysanthemums* by Fantin-Latour was the first of the seven works which the Gallery eventually acquired by this popular artist and it was the first of many fine French pictures presented by the Trustees of the Hamilton Bequest.

The Hamilton Trust[15] was created to give effect to the wishes of a Glasgow family, John Hamilton and his sisters Elizabeth and Christina, who had connections with Kelvingrove House[16] which originally stood near the site of the present Gallery.

They bequeathed their estates 'to purchase a collection of oil paintings to be placed in the Glasgow Art Galleries and Museums at Kelvingrove'. The Trust came into operation in 1927 and ever since has played a vital role in the formation of the French and British collections. Indeed the very first Impressionist picture acquired by Kelvingrove was Monet's *Ventimiglia* which the Trust bought in 1943. Since then a further 14 French paintings have been presented including works by Sisley, Cassatt, Pissarro, Gauguin, Signac, Marquet and Camoin. Along with James Donald and William McInnes (see p00) the Hamilton Bequest is therefore one of the French collection's three greatest benefactors.

In the 1930s more Barbizon pictures were added including a delightful landscape by Harpignies, presented by the Hamilton Trust, and in 1939, the bequest of William J Chrystal[17] was received. This group of one Scottish and nine French pictures, which includes good examples of the work of Daubigny, Fantin-Latour, Lhermitte and Monticelli, again reflects the popularity of Barbizon and realist art with late 19th century Scottish collectors. Chrystal is one of the very few benefactors whose purchase records have come to light and they reveal that he bought these paintings between 1889 and 1915, mostly from Glasgow dealers such as Connell, Anderson, Silva White and van Baerle.

By the late 1930s a broad representation of good quality Barbizon, realist and other mid-19th century French works had been acquired, forming an appropriate basis for the Impressionist and Post-impressionist pictures that began to arrive in the 1940s. The Director of Glasgow Museums and Art Galleries from 1939 to 1954, Dr T J Honeyman (1891-1971), was responsible for building up the later French collection as his over-riding interest was in painting of this period. Having been a dealer with the firm of Alex. Reid and Lefevre in the 1930s he had good connections with the trade and with collectors and fortunately he was Director at a time when prices were low – in 1942 he bought Derain's *Blackfriars* for £142.

The 1940s were undoubtedly the richest years in the formation of Glasgow's French collection. The start of the decade was marked with a gift from William McInnes,[18] a Glasgow ship-owner, to commemorate the appointment of Dr Honeyman. The painting, Matisse's *Head of a girl,* was the first important 20th century French work acquired by the Gallery and surprisingly it pre-dated the arrival of all the Impressionist pictures. In 1944 McInnes died, leaving to the city his entire collection of over 70 French and Scottish paintings, along with prints, drawings, porcelain, silver and glass. The 33 French pictures in the bequest cover a wide range of styles from pre-impressionism through Impressionism itself to Neo- and Post-Impressionism, and on to Fauvism and Cubism. Among the artists whose works are included are Boudin, Monet, Degas, Renoir, Seurat, van Gogh, Cézanne, Matisse, Vuillard, Braque and Picasso. As most of these movements and painters had not previously been represented at Kelvingrove, this bequest was of the greatest importance. Unlike some collectors McInnes, a quiet man who had a genuine love of music and art, did not buy to impress but purchased only pictures which he liked, and which were appropriate to his domestic setting. His taste was impeccable and while none of his paintings are major masterpieces many are little gems of top quality such as the two tiny Seurat sketches, van Gogh's *Le Moulin de Blute-Fin, Montmartre,* the still-life by Cézanne and the Paris-period Picasso. McInnes was also a patron of living artists and he bought many works by the Glasgow Boys and the Scottish Colourists.

As with the Donald collection the pictures in the McInnes Bequest reflect the interests not only of the collector but also of the dealers who influenced his choice. In this case the dealers were Alexander Reid[19] – who was selling Impressionist paintings in Glasgow as early as the 1890s – and his son A J McNeill Reid. The Gallery at Kelvingrove, as the inheritor of so many fine Scottish private collections, has every reason to be grateful for the taste and discernment with which Reid and his partners guided their customers, among whom was also William Burrell. The French pictures which McInnes bought from Reid included Monet's *Vétheuil* and Matisse's still life *The pink table-cloth.*

Apart from the McInnes Collection, the 1940s were rich in acquisitions from other sources. The Hamilton Trust presented six paintings, among them a Monet, a Sisley, an early Signac and Gauguin's *Oestervold Park, Copenhagen.* Also during the 1940s the Gallery purchased Derain's *Blackfriars,* one of the artist's Fauve series of the Thames which were commissioned by the Paris dealer Vollard in 1906. Towards the end of the decade four French pictures were presented by Sir John Richmond,[20] a leading figure in the Glasgow business world. The first Impressionist painting to enter Richmond's collection was *The Tuileries Gardens* (1900) by Pissarro, which he bought from Alexander Reid in 1911 and nine years later he made from the same dealer one of his very finest purchases, namely Vuillard's exquisite *Mother and baby.* Both these

works, plus landscapes by Vollon and Le Sidaner and a number of British pictures, came to Glasgow in 1948.

It is however surprising to discover that alongside such spendid paintings a large number of depressingly undistinguished works was also acquired by the Gallery in the 1930s and 40s. These items, all by minor late 19th century or contemporary artists, came by gift, bequest and purchase. Although there may at the time have been pressing reasons for accepting the donated works it is particularly hard now to understand the reasons for the purchases. This contrast between the very good and the indifferent is typical of the French collection which contains not only very many fine works but also a fair number of poor quality ones.

By the end of the 1940s the nature and scope of Kelvingrove's French collection as it exists today was determined and although many pictures have been added since, these have tended to augment, or fill gaps in, existing areas rather than to extend in new directions. However, although the 1940s stand out as the richest decade, the 1950s continued the trend in quality if not in quantity. Major gifts came from the Trustees of the late David W T Cargill[21] and from the Hamilton Bequest. The Cargill gift of 1950 consisted of three outstanding works, namely *Mademoiselle de Foudras* which is one of Corot's rare portraits, Courbet's large flower piece of 1863 and a figure study by Seurat. The Hamilton Trust continued their support by presenting an early Pissarro, *The towpath,* and works by Guillaumin, Marquet, Camoin and Mary Cassatt. This last, *The sisters,* is one of the most popular paintings in the entire municipal collection. Other important gifts were two works by the Cubist painter and great teacher André Lhote, a Cézanne landscape, and a fine Rouault presented by Mrs E M Macdonald in memory of her late husband Duncan, one time partner in Reid & Lefevre. Purchases during the decade included paintings by Rousseau, Vlaminck, Friesz and Marcoussis.

The 1960s, 70s and 80s have seen a further drop in the quantity of French paintings entering the collection and this is of course largely due to the phenomenal increases in price of 19th and 20th century French art. Nevertheless some pictures have been added over the last 25 years including a few major works. In the 1960s Mr and Mrs A J McNeill Reid donated a landscape by Dufy, and the Hamilton Trust presented a work by Moret, the last French picture which they have bought to date.

In 1974 the Gallery's debt to Alexander Reid was commemorated by the purchase of his portrait by van Gogh. This picture was painted in Paris in 1887 during the artist's brief experiment with Neo-Impressionism. At that time Vincent was living with his brother Theo who worked for the dealer Boussod and Valadon, successor to Goupil. (Vincent had earlier been employed by Goupil in The Hague, London and Paris.) In 1887 Reid was also working at this gallery and it is said that he and Vincent shared rooms for a while.[22] This portrait was the most expensive item ever bought for Glasgow's fine art collection and its purchase was made possible only by a special Government grant, the National Art-Collections Fund and donations from a public appeal. It is a fitting tribute to the man whose taste indirectly formed a substantial part of Glasgow's French collection.

Other paintings acquired in the 1970s include two works presented by H M Government who had accepted them in lieu of estate duty. These are a small still-life by the Cubist Juan Gris and an important Neo-Impressionist work painted by Signac in 1890. This picture, *Sunset at Herblay,* filled a conspicuous gap as the other pictures in the Gallery by Seurat and Signac are not in the pure pointillist style.

A recent addition to the French collection is *The reapers,* painted in 1860 by Jules Breton, an important realist artist. This harvest scene complements the existing group of peasant pictures by Millet, Lhermitte, Bastien-Lepage and others. *The reapers* was bought in 1984 with the assistance of the Government's Local Museums Purchase Fund, the National Art-Collections Fund, The Pilgrim Trust, Glasgow Art Gallery and Museums Association, an anonymous donor and public subscription.

As this catalogue goes to press, the gallery has just purchased, with the aid of the Local Museums Purchase Fund, a landscape painted in 1889 by Emile Bernard, one of the followers of Gauguin at Pont-Aven in the 1880s. This picture is an important acquisition as the work of the Symbolists was not previously represented at Kelvingrove.

In the past Glasgow acquired a splendid collection of works by the Impressionists, their predecessors and their immediate successors. These paintings came largely through gifts and bequests but times have changed and major donations of this type are rarely forthcoming. Like most other galleries, for important acquisitions Glasgow now has to rely more and more on outside sources, such as those named above, to supplement the Local Authority's purchase grant; the general public has been generous in responding to appeals and hopefully in the future business patronage will also be attracted. There are still many gaps to fill, even in existing strong areas of the collection – which surprisingly lacks an Impressionist painting dating from the 1870s, the most crucial decade in the development of the movement. The early, vital period of Cubism is totally unrepresented as are near contemporary expressionists like Chagall and Soutine. Although there are abundant holdings of Barbizon and realist pictures the major academic Salon painters of the day such as Bouguereau and Cabanel are totally absent. And of course pre-19th century art is almost non-existent. It is therefore to be hoped that funds will be found to continue to expand the country's finest municipal collection of French paintings.

Anne Donald

Notes

1 Archibald McLellan (1797-1854). See Elspeth Gallie: *Archibald McLellan* in *The Scottish Art Review,* vol V no 1, 1954, pp7-12.

2 Neither the first catalogue (published in 1855), nor an early ledger, nor the Gallery's register (which was probably not begun until after 1882) lists the entire bequest of 510 pictures. Owing to the sales in 1872, 1878 and 1882 and to an exchange of items with the Imperial Museum in Tokyo in 1879, not all the pictures in the bequest are still in the Gallery.

3 Subsequent 19th and early 20th century catalogues often add to the confusion (see note 2 above) as a new numbering system was adopted each time and attributions were changed without cross-references. (Not until 1935 was a catalogue produced in which the Gallery's permanent register numbers were used.)

4 William Euing (1788-1874), one of Glasgow's leading underwriters in marine insurance. See *Memoirs and portraits of one hundred Glasgow men,* vol I, 1886, pp123-6.

5 Adam Teacher (1838/39-1898), wine merchant in Glasgow.

6 John Graham-Gilbert RSA (1794-1866). His widow bequeathed his collection in 1877. See *Memoirs and portraits of one hundred Glasgow men*, vol I, 1886, pp145-8.

7 William Buchanan: *Memoirs of... the importation of pictures by the great masters*, 2 vols (London 1824). See also Hugh Brigstocke: *William Buchanan and the 19th century art trade* (1982).

8 Algernon Graves: *Art sales from early in the 18th century to early in the 20th century* (1918-1921, reprinted 1973).

9 James Reid JP (1823-1894) chief director and sole partner for many years of Neilson, Reid & Co, Hydepark Locomotive Works, Glasgow, the largest locomotive manufacturers in Europe. Ten French and British pictures from his collection were presented by his family. See *Glasgow contemporaries at the dawn of the twentieth century* (nd) p218.

10 John Forbes White LLD (1831-1904), an Aberdeen miller and art collector, brought *Pastorale* to Scotland in 1874, the year after it was painted. He owned a second work by Corot (unidentified).

11 Daniel Cottier (1838-1891). On Cottier and the late 19th century Glasgow art dealing scene in general see Richard Marks: *Burrell, portrait of a collector* (Glasgow 1983) pp58-64; Brian Gould: *Two van Gogh contacts:– E. J. van Wisselingh and Daniel Cottier* (London 1969) and Ronald Pickvance: *A man of influence: Alex Reid* (Scottish Arts Council 1967), all with further bibliographies.

12 Craibe Angus (1830-1899). His daughter married the Dutch dealer Elbert van Wisselingh. See Marks and Gould (note 11 above).

13 James Donald (1830-1905) born in Bothwell, partner in the Glasgow chemical manufacturing firm of George Miller & Co. See *The Glasgow Herald* 25 March 1905 (obituary).

14 One of these, the Morton or Dalmahoy *Portrait of Mary Queen of Scots*, was thought at the time of its purchase in 1926 to be an important late 16th century French work but it is now considered British and possibly of later date.

15 See *The Hamilton Bequest 1927-1977* (Glasgow Art Gallery & Museum 1977).

16 Built 1783 as a private house to a design by Robert Adam on the site now occupied by the tennis courts near the present Gallery. From c1870 used as the city's museum (a wing was added in 1876) until its demolition to make way for the 1901 International Exhibition although the wing remained standing for longer.

17 William James Chrystal (1854-1921) chairman of the chemical manufacturing firm J & J White Ltd. Lived latterly at Auchendennan House, near Balloch, on Loch Lomondside. His will stated that, after several liferents, Glasgow Art Gallery was to be given the choice of ten items from his large collection of 19th and 20th century French and British pictures. See *The Glasgow Herald* 22 April 1921 (obituary).

18 William McInnes (1868-1944), partner in the Glasgow shipping firm of Gow, Harrison & Co. See *The Glasgow Herald* 30 March 1944 (obituary) and T J Honeyman *Art and audacity* (Glasgow 1971) pp124-6.

19 Alexander Reid (1854-1928) founded *La Société des Beaux Arts* as a commercial gallery in Glasgow in 1889. In 1913 his son A J McNeill Reid (1893-1972) joined the firm. Thirteen years later a merger took place with the Lefevre Gallery in London and Alex. Reid retired. In 1931 the Glasgow branch closed and the London firm eventually dropped the name Alex. Reid. See Pickvance and Marks (note 11 above).

20 Sir John Richmond (1869-1963), senior deputy chairman of the Glasgow engineering firm G & J Weir. He endowed the Richmond Chair of Fine Art at Glasgow University. The remainder of his collection was presented to the National Gallery of Scotland by his niece Mrs Isabel Traill. See Hugh Brigstocke: *French and Scottish paintings – The Richmond-Traill Collection* (NGS 1980).

21 David William Traill Cargil (1872-1939), son of the founder of, and for many years himself associated with, the Burmah Oil Company. Also had business interests in India. Formed one of the finest collections of Impressionist and later French painting ever assembled in Scotland. Most of the pictures were sold after his death and

the proceeds used to form the Cargill Fund, a trust which gives assistance to Scottish charities and artistic organisations. See *The Glasgow Herald* 7 September 1939 (obituary) and Honeyman (note 18 above).

22 See Pickvance (note 11 above) pp7-9 and T J Honeyman: *A link with Glasgow* in *The Scottish Art Review,* vol II, no 2, 1948, pp16-21.

Catalogue Notes

Every picture is illustrated, in alphabetical order of artists' surnames. Several works by the same artist are given in register number order, with autograph works preceding those of doubtful attribution.

Titles remain unchanged since the 1967 catalogue except where an artist's original title has been discovered or a landscape re-identified. All titles are in English, apart from a few place names.

A date is given only if a picture is either dated by the artist or if other good authority (eg catalogue raisonné) for the date exists.

All pictures are in oil unless otherwise stated.

Sizes are in inches, followed by centimetres, with height preceding width. Where a picture is signed, the precise form of the signature is given.

The names of donors of more than six items to the French collection are given in abbreviated form in the captions. Full details of these bequests are as follows:
Archibald McLellan 1854
William Euing 1874
Adam Teacher 1898
James Donald 1905
William J Chrystal 1939
William McInnes 1944

Each caption concludes with the picture's register number.

Attributions

A number of works have been re-attributed since the publication of the 1967 catalogue from which many problematic pictures were omitted. Many curators and art historians have helped the author with attributions and they will be fully acknowledged when a text volume is produced. Hesitancy as to the rightness of an attribution is marked by the use of the following words, as defined in the Gallery's 1961 catalogue of *Dutch and Flemish Paintings:*

Ascribed to   indicates that either the traditional attribution or that given in the previous catalogue (1967) is followed with reserve.

Attributed to is used in the case of a picture attributed to an artist by the present cataloguer either independently or following some other writer.

Studio of   means that a picture appears to have been produced in the workshop of a particular painter, probably under his supervision and following his design.

After   indicates that a picture is a copy, whether contemporary with the artist concerned or not.

Imitator of is self-explanatory, though an intended deceit is not necessarily implied.

Follower of means the work of a pupil, or another, working in the manner or tradition of the master referred to, though not purely imitatively, at a similar or later date.

Style of   suggests no more than a tenuous relationship.

Edmond Marthe Alphonse ANDRE 1837-1877
Awaiting orders
canvas 19×38⅝ (48.2×98.2) signed: *Edmond André*
Teacher Bequest 1898
811

Jules BASTIEN-LEPAGE 1848-1884
Poor Fauvette
canvas 64×49½ (162.5×125.7) signed: *J. BASTIEN-LEPAGE/DAMVILLERS 1881*
Purchased 1913
1323

Hugues de BEAUMONT   1874-1948
Still-life
wood 6⅞×7¾ (17.5×19.8) signed: *Hugues de Beaumont*
McInnes Bequest 1944
2375

ascribed to Camille Félix BELLANGER   1853-1923 and
Matthijs MARIS Dutch 1839-1917
Diana
canvas 78½×40⅞ (199.4×103.8) unsigned
Presented by William Milne 1927
1727
According to old records, Maris substantially overpainted
this work, possibly by C F Bellanger, for the dealer Cottier
in London

Emile BERNARD 1868-1941
Landscape, Saint-Briac
canvas, 21¼×25¼ (54×65) signed: *EB '89*
Purchased 1985 with the aid of the
Government's Local Museums Purchase Fund.
3401

Pierre BILLET 1837-1922
Bringing in the catch
canvas 46¼×72 (117.5×182.9) signed: *Pierre Billet 1885*
Presented by Miss Kirkpatrick 1947
2632

attributed to Louis Gabriel BLANCHET 1705-1777
Portrait of Archibald Stuart of Torrance (d.1767)
canvas 49½×39½ (125.7×99.9) unsigned
Purchased 1961
3150

Pierre BONNARD 1867-1947
Edge of the forest *c*1919
wood 14⅝×18¹/₁₆ (37.2×45.9) signed: *Bonnard*
McInnes Bequest 1944
2376

François Saint BONVIN 1817-1887
Still-life
canvas 12⅝×15⅞ (32.1×40.3) signed: *F. Bonvin, 1876*
McInnes Bequest 1944
2377

François Saint BONVIN 1817-1887
Interior with old woman kneeling
wood 14¾×11¼ (37.4×28.6) signed: *François Bonvin, 1854*
Presented by T Craig Annan 1950
2853

after François BOUCHER 1703-1770
Sylvia saved by Amintas
canvas diameter 52¾ (134) unsigned
Purchased 1952
2958
See note to no 2959

after François BOUCHER 1703-1770
Amintas revived by Sylvia
canvas diameter 52¾ (134) unsigned
Presented by George Campbell 1952
2959
Nos 2958 and 2959 are copies of two of a series of four
compositions painted in 1755-56 for the Hôtel de Toulouse
(now the Banque de France) in Paris. Only the first two of
the series remain there, including the original of no 2958,
while the original of no 2959 and the fourth picture are
now in the Musée des Beaux-Arts, Tours.

Eugène Louis BOUDIN 1824-1898
A street in Dordrecht
wood 16⅛×12⅞ (41×32.7) signed: *84/Boudin*
McInnes Bequest 1944
2378

Eugène Louis BOUDIN 1824-1898
The port of Deauville *c*1880-84
canvas 16⅛×21¾ (41×53.2) signed: *E. Boudin*
McInnes Bequest 1944
2379

Eugène Louis BOUDIN 1824-1898
Seascape
wood 14¾×18¼ (37.4×46.3) signed: *E. Boudin 91.*
Bequeathed by George B Dunlop 1951
2916

after Bon BOULLOGNE 1649-1717
The Annunciation
canvas 39⅛×28½ (100×72.3) unsigned
McLellan Bequest 1854
217
A copy, with variations, probably dating from the late
18th century, of a work by Boullogne in the Louvre, Paris

Georges BRAQUE 1882-1963
Still-life
wood 17⁵/₁₆×21¹/₂ (44×54.6) signed: *G. Braque 26*
McInnes Bequest 1944
2380

Jules Adolphe Aimé Louis BRETON 1827-1906
The reapers
canvas 29½×44 (74.9×111.7) signed: *Jules Breton/1860*
Purchased 1984 with the aid of the Government's Local Museums
Purchase Fund, the National Art-Collections Fund, The Pilgrim
Trust, Glasgow Art Gallery and Museums Association
and public subscription
3396

Charles CAMOIN 1879-1965
Place de Clichy, Paris *c*1907
canvas 25⅝×32 (65.1×81.3) signed: *Ch. Camoin*
Hamilton Bequest 1957
3063

Mary CASSATT 1844-1926
The sisters *c*1885
canvas 18¼×21¹³/₁₆ (46.3×55.5) signed: *Mary Cassatt*
Hamilton Bequest 1953
2980

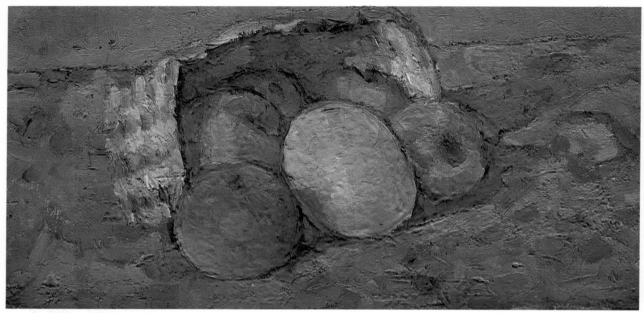

Paul CEZANNE 1839-1906
Overturned basket of fruit *c*1877
canvas 6⁵/₁₆×12³/₄ (16×32.3) unsigned
McInnes Bequest 1944
2382

Paul CEZANNE 1839-1906
La Chaine de l'Etoile avec le Pilon du Roi *c*1878-79
canvas 19⅜×23¼ (49.2×59) unsigned
Presented by Mrs Jessie McInnes 1951
2932

Jean Baptiste Camille COROT 1796-1875
Pastorale – souvenir d'Italie 1873
canvas 68×56⅞ (172.7×144.4) signed: *COROT*
Presented by the sons of James Reid of Auchterarder 1896
732

Jean Baptiste Camille COROT 1796-1875
The woodcutter 1865-70
Canvas 19⁹/₁₆×25⁹/₁₆ (49.6×64.8) signed: *COROT*
Donald Bequest 1905
115

Jean Baptiste Camille COROT 1796-1875
The crayfisher 1865-70
canvas 40¾×30 (103.5×76.2) signed: *COROT*
Donald Bequest 1905
1120

Jean Baptiste Camille COROT 1796-1875
The river-bank *c*1870
canvas 15³/₄×23¹¹/₁₆ (40.1×60.1) signed: *COROT*
McInnes Bequest 1944
2383

Jean Baptiste Camille COROT 1796-1875
Mademoiselle de Foudras 1872
canvas 35×23⅜ (88.9×59.3) signed: *COROT*
Presented by the Trustees of David W T Cargill 1950
2858

ascribed to Jean Baptiste Camille COROT 1796-1875
Wooded landscape with figures
canvas 12⅝×17⅞ (32×45.3) signed: *COROT*
Bequeathed by Mrs Isabella Elder 1906
1160

ascribed to Jean Baptiste Camille COROT 1796-1875
Evening
canvas 13×22¹¹/₁₆ (33×57.7) signed: *COROT*
Donald Bequest 1905
1112

ascribed to Jean Baptiste Camille COROT 1796-1875
The bathers
canvas 12¾×18⅛ (32.4×46.1) signed: *COROT*
Chrystal Bequest 1939
2135

ascribed to Jean Baptiste Camille COROT 1796-1875
The lake
canvas 9⅝×14 (24.4×35.5) signed: *COROT*
Donald Bequest 1905
1148

Jean Desiré Gustave COURBET 1819-1877
Apple, pear and orange 1871-72
wood 5$\frac{1}{8}$×8$\frac{1}{8}$ (13×20.7) signed: *G. Courbet.*
McInnes Bequest 1944
2384

Jean Desiré Gustave COURBET 1819-1877
Flowers in a basket
canvas 29⅞×39⅝ (75.9×100.8) signed: ..*63/Gustave Courbet.*
Presented by the Trustees of David W T Cargill 1950
2859

ascribed to Jean Desiré Gustave COURBET 1819-1877
Portrait of a woman
canvas 24×19⅝ (61×49.8) signed: *G. Courbet*
Hamilton Bequest 1948
2775

ascribed to Guillaume COURTOIS 1628-1679
The Plague at Ashdod
red chalk 16¹⁵/₁₆×19¼ (37.9×48.8)
James Campbell Collection
U.30
Inscribed on reverse: *Guill. Courtois del. after N. Poussin.*
A copy of the painting of the same title by Nicolas Poussin
in the Louvre, Paris

Pascal Adolphe Jean DAGNAN-BOUVERET 1862-1929
Portrait of a lady
canvas 20¹/₁₆×7¾ (51×19.6) signed: *PA J. DAGNAN-B*
Presented by L M Angus-Butterworth 1960
3126

Charles François DAUBIGNY 1817-1878
Lake with ducks
wood $14^{15}/_{16} \times 26^{1}/_{2}$ (37.9×67.3) signed: *Daubigny 1873*
Donald Bequest 1905
1141

Charles François DAUBIGNY 1817-1878
Seascape at Villerville 1876
wood 13×22³/₁₆ (33×56.7) unsigned
Chrystal Bequest 1939
2136

Charles François DAUBIGNY 1817-1878
River scene with wooded banks
wood 15¼×26⅜ (38.7×67) unsigned
Chrystal Bequest 1939
2137

imitator of Charles François DAUBIGNY 1817-1878
River scene, sunset
wood 10⅛×18¾ (25.7×47.6) signed: *Daubigny 1865*
Bequeathed by Rev H G Roberts Hay-Boyd 1941
2230

Honoré Victorin DAUMIER 1808-1879
The gossip *c*1870
canvas 15¾×12½ (40×31.7) unsigned
McInnes Bequest 1944
2385

Alexandre Gabriel DECAMPS 1803-1860
St Jerome in the wilderness
paper on canvas 18×27¼ (45.7×69.2) signed: *D. C. 1842*
Donald Bequest 1905
1129

Edgar Hilaire Germain DEGAS 1834-1917
Dancers on a bench *c*1898
pastel 21⅛×29¾ (53.7×75.6) signed: *Degas*
McInnes Bequest 1944
2441

studio of Ferdinand Victor Eugène DELACROIX 1798-1863
The expulsion of Adam and Eve from Paradise
canvas 53⅝×41⅜ (136.2×105.1) signed: *EUG. DELACROIX*
Hamilton Bequest 1933
1873
This picture relates to one of the cupola pendentives in the library
of the Palais Bourbon, Paris, whose decorations were painted by
Delacroix between 1838 and 1847.

André DERAIN 1880-1954
Blackfriars c1906
canvas 31¾×39⅛ (80.6×99.3) unsigned
Purchased 1942
2283

Jean Baptiste Edouard DETAILLE 1848-1912
The drummer
watercolour 8³/₄×5³/₄ (22.2×14.6)
signed: *EDOUARD DETAILLE/1882*
Bequeathed by Miss Margaret H Garroway 1947
2599

Narcisse Virgile DIAZ DE LA PENA 1808-1876
Flowerpiece
wood 14¹/₁₆×10³/₄ (35.7×27.3) signed: *N. Diaz*
Donald Bequest 1905
1114

Narcisse Virgile DIAZ DE LA PENA 1808-1876
In the forest
wood 9×14³/₈ (22.8×36.5) signed: *N. Diaz*
Donald Bequest 1905
1117

Narcisse Virgile DIAZ DE LA PENA 1808-1876
Roses and other flowers
canvas 24⅜×19½ (61.8×49.5) signed: *N. Diaz*
Bequeathed by Mrs Isabella Elder 1906
1159

Paul Gustave Louis Christophe DORE 1832-1883
Glen Massan
canvas 44³/₈×72³/₄ (112.7×184.8) signed: *G. Doré*

Presented by Dr and Mrs W Muir Robertson 1979
3352

Gabriel DUCULTIL 1878-1955
Landscape
watercolour 5×9 (12.7×22.8) signed: G. Ducultil
Presented by Mrs Lucy Laurie 1922
1536

Raoul DUFY 1877-1953
The pier at Deauville
canvas 18³/₁₆×21⁵/₈ (46.1×54.9) signed: *Raoul Dufy 1929*
Presented by Mr and Mrs A J McNeill Reid 1960
3120

Gaspar DUGHET 1615-1675
Ideal landscape *c*1655-60
canvas 36⁷⁄₈×52³⁄₈ (93.6×133) unsigned
Bequeathed by Mrs John Graham-Gilbert 1877
596

ascribed to Gaspar DUGHET 1615-1675
Italian landscape
canvas 18⅞×24⅝ (47.9×65.2) unsigned
McLellan Bequest 1854
150

follower of Gaspar DUGHET 1615-1675
Landscape with a river
canvas 18⅜×29¼ (46.3×74.3) unsigned
McLellan Bequest 1854
175

style of Gaspar DUGHET 1615-1675
Italian landscape with figures
canvas 22½×17½ (57.1×44.4) unsigned
McLellan Bequest 1854
169

Jacques Vigouroux DUPLESSIS *c*1680-*c*1730
In a notary public's office
canvas 44×76½ (111.6×194.3)
signed: *J. V. Duplessis./invenit et pinxit. 1719.*
Presented by Mrs Leadbetter 1937
2077

François Léonard DUPONT 1756-1821
The vintage
canvas 25⅛×31⅝ (63.9×80.3) unsigned
McLellan Bequest 1854
219

Jules DUPRE 1811-1889
The headland
canvas 28½×36 (72.4×91.4) signed: *Jules Dupré*
Donald Bequest 1905
1130

Léon Victor DUPRE 1816-1879
Landscape
wood 10×18 (25.4×45.7) signed: *Victor Dupré*
Presented by Alexander Hill 1922
1529

Louisa EUDES DE GUIMARD 1827-1904
Boy asleep
canvas 19$^{11}/_{16}$×23$^{7}/_{8}$ (50×60.7) signed: *L. Eudes de Guimard*
Euing Bequest 1874
435

Théophile Emmanuel DUVERGER 1821-1901
Playmates
wood 12$^{3}/_{4}$×9$^{1}/_{2}$ (32.4×24.1) signed: *DUVERGER*
Bequeathed by Mrs Isabella Elder 1906
1164

Ignace Henri Jean Théodore FANTIN-LATOUR 1836-1904
Chrysanthemums
canvas 24×19 (61×48.3) signed: *Fantin. 79*
Hamilton Bequest 1929
1795

Ignace Henri Jean Théodore FANTIN-LATOUR 1836-1904
Roses 'La France' 1895
canvas 15⅞×18⅛ (40.2×46) signed: *Fantin*
Chrystal Bequest 1939
2138

Ignace Henri Jean Théodore FANTIN-LATOUR 1836-1904
Larkspur
canvas 27×22⅞ (68.6×57.9) signed: *Fantin. 92*
Chrystal Bequest 1939
2139

Ignace Henri Jean Théodore FANTIN-LATOUR
1836-1904
The dance 1898
canvas 23⅝×28⅞ (60×73.1) signed: *Fantin*
McInnes Bequest 1944
2386

Ignace Henri Jean Théodore FANTIN-LATOUR
1836-1904
A mixed bunch
canvas 15³⁄₁₆×10¹³⁄₁₆ (38.4×27.5) signed: *Fantin. 72*
Bequeathed by George B Dunlop 1951
2917

Ignace Henri Jean Théodore FANTIN-LATOUR
1836-1904
Still-life
canvas 10⅛×12⅛ (25.7×30.7) signed: *Fantin. 77*
McInnes Bequest 1944
2387

Ignace Henri Jean Théodore FANTIN-LATOUR
1836-1904
The bathers 1883
canvas 10¾×16⅛ (27.3×41) signed: *Fantin*
Presented by Miss Rule 1951
2933

follower of Jean Honoré FRAGONARD 1732-1806
Spring
wood 12¼×7¼ (31×18.5) unsigned
Presented by F J Nettlefold 1948
2692

follower of Jean Honoré FRAGONARD 1732-1806
Summer
wood 12¼×7¾ (31×20) unsigned
Presented by F J Nettlefold 1948
2693

style of Jean Honoré FRAGONARD 1732-1806
A child's head
wood 7¼×6⅛ (18.4×15.6) unsigned
McLellan Bequest 1854
225

follower of Jean Honoré FRAGONARD 1732-1806
Autumn
wood 12¼×7¼ (31×18.5) unsigned
Presented by F J Nettlefold 1948
2694

Pierre Edouard FRERE 1819-1886
Mother and children
wood 18×14¾ (45.7×37.5) signed: *Edouard Frère. 1877.*
Donald Bequest 1905
1134

Achille Emile Othon FRIESZ 1879-1949
The Seine at Paris – Pont de Grenelle 1901
canvas 18⅛×13¹/₁₆ (46.2×33.1) signed: *E. Othon Friesz*
Purchased 1959
3110

Paul GAUGUIN   1848-1903
Oestervold Park, Copenhagen
canvas 23¼×28⅝ (59.1×72.7)   signed: *P. Gauguin 85*
Hamilton Bequest 1944
2465

Paul GAVARNI (Hippolyte-Sulpice CHEVALIER)
1804-1866
Boy beating a drum
red chalk and pencil 7⅝×5⁵/₁₆ (19.4×13.5)
signed: *Edimbourg 49/Gavarni*
Provenance unrecorded
U.29

Lucien GERARD 19th century
Young man reading
wood 8¾×6¾ (22.2×17.1) signed: *Lucien Gerard*
Bequeathed by Miss Margaret H Garroway 1947
2600

Vincent van GOGH 1853-1890
Le Moulin de Blute-Fin, Montmartre 1886
canvas 17⅞×14¾ (45.4×37.5) signed: *Vincent*
McInnes Bequest 1944
2425

Vincent van GOGH 1853-1890
Portrait of Alexander Reid (1854-1928) 1887
board 16½×13 (42×33) signed: *Vincent*
Purchased 1974 with the aid of a special Government grant,
the National Art-Collections Fund, an anonymous donor and
public subscription
3315

Lucien Henri GRANDGERARD 1880-?
Adolescence
paper on wood 26³/₈×19⁵/₈ (67×49.8)
signed: *L. Grandgerard/35*
Purchased 1938
2116

after Jean Baptiste GREUZE 1725-1805
The sulky boy
canvas 15×11 (38×27.9)
Euing Bequest 1874
433
A copy of the painting in the Musée Cognacq-Jay, Paris

Juan (José Victoriano Gonzalez) GRIS 1887-1927
The glass 1918
canvas 10½×6¼ (26.7×15.9) signed: *Juan Gris*
Presented by H M Government, by whom accepted in lieu of estate duty, 1976
3329

Paul Louis Narcisse GROLLERON 1848-1901
The scout
wood 6¼×8⅝ (15.9×21.9) signed: *P. Grolleron 81*
Bequeathed by Miss Margaret H Garroway 1947
2601

Jean Baptiste Armand GUILLAUMIN 1841-1927
River bank, autumn
canvas 25⅛×31½ (64×80) signed: *Guillaumin*
Hamilton Bequest 1951
2897

Jean Baptiste Armand GUILLAUMIN 1841-1927
The coast at St Palais 1893
canvas 25⅝×31⅞ (65.1×80.9) signed: *Guillaumin* inscribed on reverse: *St Palais. aout 93. 3ème soir*
Purchased 1951
2909

Henri Joseph HARPIGNIES 1819-1916
Moonrise
canvas 20¾×33³/₁₆ (52.7×84.2) signed: *H J Harpignies. 92.*
Hamilton Bequest 1932
1832

Henri Joseph HARPIGNIES 1819-1916
Chestnut trees at Briare, sunset
watercolour 7⅝×10⅞ (19.4×27.6)
signed: *H. J Harpignies 88.*
Bequeathed by Rev H G Roberts Hay-Boyd 1941
2235

Henri Joseph HARPIGNIES 1819-1916
'Les Roches', Briare
watercolour 9⅞×13⅞ (25.2×35.2) signed: *H J Harpignies*
Bequeathed by Miss Edith M Robinson 1962
62-3

Henri Joseph HARPIGNIES 1819-1916
Path at St Privé
charcoal 9×11⅝ (22.8×29.5) signed: *H J Harpignies 1910*
Bequeathed by Miss Catherine Howden 1925
25-26gk

Louis Henri Victor Jules Adolphe HERVIER 1818-1879
Village scene, Barbizon
wood 5^1/$_{16}$×12^1/$_8$ (12.9×30.8) signed: *HERVIER*
McInnes Bequest 1944
2389

Georges Louis HYON 1840-1909
An episode in the Franco-Prussian War
canvas 36⅜×47 (92.4×119.4) signed: *G. HYON.*
Bequeathed by Major John Garroway 1920
1495

Charles Emile JACQUE 1813-1894
The wane of day
canvas 28⅜×39⅛ (72.1×99.4) signed: *Ch. Jacque 1881*
Presented by the sons of James Reid of Auchterarder 1896
740

Charles Emile JACQUE 1813-1894
Study of a shepherdess
charcoal 11⅛×6½ (28.3×16.5) signed: *Ch. Jacque*
Purchased 1964
64-3

Johann Barthold JONGKIND 1819-1891
Winter scene in Holland
wood 5$\frac{11}{16}$×9$\frac{1}{8}$ (14.4×23.2) signed: *Jongkind 1865*
McInnes Bequest 1944
2400

Johann Barthold JONGKIND 1819-1891
View of Paris
watercolour 6³/₁₆×13¹/₁₆ (15.7×33.2)
signed: *Paris 1879 Jongkind*
McInnes Bequest 1944
2435

Madeleine Camille JULLIOTTE 1887-1948
Market in Spain 1928
wood 12⁷/₈×16¹/₁₆ (32.7×40.8) signed: *Made Julliott*
Bequeathed by Miss Mary R Lang 1960
3132

Charles Louis KRATKE 1848-1921
French army on the march
canvas 20⁷/₈×27³/₄ (53×70.5) signed: *KRATKE 1877*
Bequeathed by Miss Margaret H Garroway 1947
2602

attributed to Charles François LACROIX DE MARSEILLE
*c*1700-1782
Seascape – a storm
canvas 10×14¹/₂ (25.4×36.8) unsigned
Bequeathed by Sir Claude Phillips 1924
1589

Eugène Galien LALOUE 1854-1941
Le Boulevard de la Madeleine, Paris
gouache 19½×39 (49.5×99) signed: *E. Galien-Laloue*
Bequeathed by Jonathan Leslie Dean 1927
1695

Emile Charles LAMBINET 1815-1877
Sea coast scene
canvas 29¼×54⅞ (74.3×139.4)
signed: *1867. Emile Lambinet*
Bequeathed by Mrs Isabella Elder 1906
1157

ascribed to Jacques Sebastien LECLERC *c*1734-1785
Summer
wood 10⅝×14 (27×35.6) unsigned
Euing Bequest 1874
420

ascribed to Jacques Sebastien LECLERC *c*1734-1785
Autumn
wood 10⅝×14 (27×35.6) unsigned
Euing Bequest 1874
411

Paul Emile LECOMTE 1877-1950
The end of the market, Grenada
canvas 25½×31¾ (65×80.8) signed: *Paul Emile Lecomte*
Purchased 1937
2083

Alphonse LEGROS 1837-1911
An approaching storm
canvas 33½×44 (85×111.8) signed: *A. Legros 1897*
Presented by R D Macgregor 1919
1463

Alphonse LEGROS 1837-1911
Peasants in a landscape
sepia 14½×21⅞ (36.8×55.6) signed: *A. Legros*
Presented by W Y Macgregor 1924
24-4a

Alphonse LEGROS 1837-1911
Farm at Roujan
watercolour 17⅛×25¼ (43.5×64.1) signed: *A. Legros*
Presented by W Y Macgregor 1924
24-4

Alphonse LEGROS 1837-1911
Edge of the wood
sepia 11⅝×18½ (29.5×47) signed: *A. Legros*
Presented by Guy Knowles 1953
53-3

Alphonse LEGROS 1837-1911
Terrified bacchantes
bistre 10¼×15¾ (26×40) signed with monogram: *AL*
Presented by Guy Knowles 1953
53-3a

Théophile Victor Emile LEMMENS 1821-1867
Poultry
canvas 9½×12⅞ (24.1×32.7) signed: *1857. E. LEMMENS*
Teacher Bequest 1898
837

after François LEMOINE 1688-1737
The guilt of Callisto
canvas 29⅜×36⅜ (74.5×92.4) unsigned
McLellan Bequest 1854
48
A copy of a work signed and dated 1727(?) in a private
collection

after François LEMOINE 1688-1737
Hercules and Omphale
canvas 27×21½ (68.6×54.6) unsigned
Purchased 1953
2999
A copy, in reverse, with alterations, of a painting by
Lemoine in the Louvre, Paris

Stanislas Victor Edmond Lepine 1835-1892
La rue de Norvins, Montmartre
canvas 12⅝×9¼ (32.1×23.5) signed: *S. Lépine*
McInnes Bequest 1944
2401

Henri Eugène Augustin LE SIDANER 1862-1939
Square in Beauvais, moonlight
canvas 27⅝×36⅜ (70.2×92.4) signed: *LE SIDANER 1900*
Bequeathed by Dr David Perry 1940
2193

Henri Eugène Augustin LE SIDANER 1862-1939
Nemours 1903
pastel 19¾×24 (50.2×61) signed: *LE SIDANER*
Presented by Sir John Richmond 1948
2812

Léon Augustin LHERMITTE 1844-1925
Evening work
canvas 36¾×48 (93.3×122) signed: *L. Lhermitte. 1888.*
Chrystal Bequest 1939
2140

Léon Augustin LHERMITTE 1844-1925
The weaver 1882
charcoal 19¼×24⅞ (48.9×63.2) signed: *L. Lhermitte*
Presented by A B Clements 1940
2165

Léon Augustin LHERMITTE 1844-1925
Ploughing with oxen *c*1871
canvas 23⅝×40½ (60×102.9) signed: *Léon Lhermitte*
Bequeathed by Rev H G Roberts Hay-Boyd 1941
2229

Léon Augustin LHERMITTE 1844-1925
The bather
pastel 34×44½ (86.4×113) signed: *L. Lhermitte/1907*
Presented by F J Nettlefold 1948
2690

André LHOTE 1885-1962
Negress
canvas 13⁷/₈×10⁵/₈ (35.2×27) signed: *A. LHOTE*
Presented by John Mathias 1951
2930

André LHOTE 1885-1962
Nude
canvas 28⅝×23¼ (72.7×59) signed: *A. LHOTE*
Presented by John Mathias 1951
2931

Maximilien LUCE 1858-1941
Landscape with willow trees
canvas 29⅝×24⅛ (50×61.3) signed: *Luce 87*
Purchased 1975 with the aid of the Lady Moore Bequest and the
Government's Local Museums Purchase Fund
3318

Louis Casimir Ladislas MARCOUSSIS 1878-1941
Table on the balcony
canvas 39⅜×25⅝ (100×65.1) signed: *Marcoussis 28*
Purchased 1951
2902

Pierre Albert MARQUET 1875-1947
Algiers harbour
canvas 21¼×25⅝ (54×65.1) signed: *Marquet*
Hamilton Bequest 1955
4030

MASTER OF MOULINS active *c*1480-*c*1500
St Maurice (or St Victor) with a donor
wood 23×19½ (58.4×49.5) unsigned
McLellan Bequest 1854
203

Jules MASURE 1819-1910
Sunset
canvas 34⅝×46⅜ (87.9×117.8) signed: *Masure*
Presented by Rev John Moore 1943
2346

Henri MATISSE 1869-1954
Head of a young girl *c*1919
canvas on cardboard 16$^{1}/_{16}$×12$^{7}/_{8}$ (40.8×32.7) signed: *Henri Matisse*
Presented by William McInnes 1940
2197

Henri MATISSE 1869-1954
The pink table-cloth 1925
canvas 23¾×31¹⁵/₁₆ (60.3×81) signed: *Henri Matisse*
McInnes Bequest 1944
2402

Paul MAZE 1887-1979
Regatta at Meulan
canvas 17×28⅝ (43.2×72.7) signed: *Paul Maze.*
Presented by The Contemporary Art Society 1940
2200

Jean Louis Ernest MEISSONIER 1815-1891
The musician
wood 18⅛×14 (46×35.6) signed: *Meissonier/1888*
Bequeathed by Captain R Allan Ogg 1943
2330

Louis METTLING 1847-1904
Woman cooking at a stove
canvas 18×15 (45.7×38.1) signed: *Mettling*
Bequeathed by John Fleming 1923
1561

Louis METTLING 1847-1904
Boy's head
canvas 21⅞×18⅛ (55.5×46.1) signed: *Mettling*
Bequeathed by Dr David Perry 1940
2189

Georges MICHEL 1763-1843
Landscape with cottages
paper on canvas 30⅞×39 (78.4×99) unsigned
Purchased 1959
3111

Gregoire MICHONZE 1902-1982
Children at play
canvas 14¾×17¾ (37.5×45.1) signed: *Michonze 46-47*
Purchased 1949
2825

Jean-François MILLET 1814-1875
Going to work 1850-51
canvas 21⅞×18⅛ (55.5×46) unsigned
Donald Bequest 1905
1111

Jean-François MILLET 1814-1875
The sheepfold 1868
charcoal and pastel 28³⁄₈×37¹⁄₁₆ (72.1×95) signed: *J. F. Millet*
Donald Bequest 1905
1119

Claude Oscar MONET 1840-1926
View of Ventimiglia
canvas 25⅝×36⅛ (65.1×91.7) signed: *Claude Monet 84*
Hamilton Bequest 1943
2336

Claude Oscar MONET 1840-1926
Vétheuil *c*1880
canvas 23½×31½ (59.7×80) signed: *Claude Monet*
McInnes Bequest 1944
2403

Pierre Eugène MONTEZIN 1874-1946
The meadow in June
canvas 45×57⅝ (114.3×146.4) signed: *Montezin/1937*
Purchased 1937
2084

Adolphe Joseph Thomas MONTICELLI 1824-1886
The marriage procession
canvas 19⅝×39¼ (49.7×99.7) signed: *Monticelli*
Bequeathed by Archibald R Henderson 1901
939

Adolphe Joseph Thomas MONTICELLI 1824-1886
The adoration of the Magi
canvas 19¾×39¼ (50.2×99.7) unsigned
Donald Bequest 1905
1135

Adolphe Joseph Thomas MONTICELLI 1824-1886
Garden fête: the white horse
wood 15¾×23¼ (40×59) unsigned
Presented by James Carfrae Alston 1909
1236

Adolphe Joseph Thomas MONTICELLI 1824-1886
Fête champêtre
canvas 19×26 (48.2×66) unsigned
Chrystal Bequest 1939
2141

Adolphe Joseph Thomas MONTICELLI 1824-1886
The orange game
wood 10¹/₁₆×20⅝ (25.6×52.4) signed: *Monticelli*
Chrystal Bequest 1939
2142

Adolphe Joseph Thomas MONTICELLI 1824-1886
Ladies of quality
wood 5⅝×11 (14.3×27.9) signed: *Monticelli*
McInnes Bequest 1944
2404

Henry MORET 1856-1913
Cliffs at Port Domois, Belle-Ile *c*1890
canvas 28⅝×23½ (72.7×59.7) signed: *Henry Moret*
Hamilton Bequest 1962
3168

Charles Joseph NATOIRE 1700-1777
Bacchantes and satyrs
canvas 25×36 (63.5×91.4) unsigned
McLellan Bequest 1854
176

Léopold PASCAL 1900-1962
La Grand'Rue, Morlaix
cardboard 14×10 (35.6×25.4) signed: *Pascal*
Purchased 1943
2348

after Pierre PARROCEL 1670-1739
Portrait of George Keith, 10th Earl Marischal (1694-1778)
canvas 29⅝×24½ (75.2×62.2) unsigned
Presented by Charles J C Douglas 1902
1017
A copy of part of a threequarter length portrait of which
several versions exist, including one in the Scottish
National Portrait Gallery, Edinburgh.

Léopold PASCAL 1900-1962
A river scene 1940-45
cardboard triptych 23¼×16½, 23¼×33, 23¼×16½ (59×41.9, 59×83.8, 59×41.9)
signed: *Pascal* with cross of Lorraine
Presented by the artist 1946
2553

style of Pierre PATEL I *c*1606-1676
Landscape with classical ruins
canvas 37⅞×53½ (96.2×135.9) unsigned
Purchased 1918
1451

Eugène PAVY   19th century
An Eastern market place
canvas 33½×50⅝ (85×128.6) signed: *Eug. Pavy. 1885.*
Teacher Bequest 1898
774

Eugène PAVY   19th century
Eastern courtyard scene
wood 19½×24 (49.5×60.9) signed: *Eug. Pavy. 1887*
Teacher Bequest 1898
836

Eugène PAVY   19th century
Eastern scene
canvas 20×25 (50.8×63.5) signed: *Eug. Pavy. 1885*
Teacher Bequest 1898
871

Philippe PAVY 1860 – ?
The toast
cardboard 8⅝×6¾ (21.9×17.1) signed: *PH. PAVY/1880*
Teacher Bequest 1898
818

Philippe PAVY 1860 – ?
A Moroccan soldier
wood 15×7⅞ (38.1×20) signed: *PH. PAVY/1885*
Teacher Bequest 1898
839

Philippe PAVY 1860 – ?
The connoisseur
wood 10×6⅞ (25.4×17.5) signed: *PH. PAVY/1881*
Teacher Bequest 1898
827

Pablo PICASSO 1881-1973
The flower seller 1901
millboard 13¼×20½ (33.7×52.1) signed: *Picasso*
McInnes Bequest 1944
2417

Camille Jacob PISSARRO 1830-1903
Tuileries Gardens
canvas 29×36⁵/₁₆ (73.6×92.3) signed: *C. Pissarro 1900.*
Presented by Sir John Richmond 1948
2811

Camille Jacob PISSARRO 1830-1903
The tow-path
canvas 32¼×42½ (81.9×107.9) signed: *C. Pissarro 1864.*
Hamilton Bequest 1951
2934

attributed to Pierre-Antoine QUILLARD *c*1704-1733
Arrival at the Island of Cythera
canvas 10⅜×12⅞ (26.9×32.1) unsigned
McLellan Bequest 1854
227

Léon RENI-MEL b. 1893
Old Vannes
canvas 29⅝×43½ (75.2×110.5) signed: *Reni-Mel 1936*
Purchased 1938
2117

Pierre Auguste RENOIR 1841-1919
The painter's garden, Cagnes *c*1908
canvas 13¹/₁₆×18¹/₈ (33.2×46) signed: *Renoir*
McInnes Bequest 1944
2418

Pierre Auguste RENOIR 1841-1919
Portrait of Madame Charles Fray (1870-1943)
canvas 25½×21¼ (64.8×54) signed: *Renoir. 01.*
McInnes Bequest 1944
2419

Pierre Auguste RENOIR 1841-1919
Still-life *c*1908
canvas 6¼×10 (15.9×25.4) signed: *Renoir* inscribed on reverse: *Cagnes 1908*
McInnes Bequest 1944
2420

Georges ROUAULT 1871-1958
Circus girl
paper on canvas 25⁵/₁₆×17¹³/₁₆ (64.3×45.3) signed: *G Rouault*
Presented by Mrs Elizabeth M Macdonald in memory of her
husband Duncan M Macdonald 1959
3101

Pierre Etienne Théodore ROUSSEAU 1812-1867
The heath
canvas 11⁹/₁₆×13 (29.4×33) signed: *TH. Rousseau*
Donald Bequest 1905
1122

Pierre Etienne Théodore ROUSSEAU 1812-1867
The forest of Clairbois *c*1836-39
canvas 25¾×41 (65.4×104.1) signed: *TH. Rousseau*
Donald Bequest 1905
1124

Pierre Etienne Théodore ROUSSEAU 1812-1867
Les gorges d'Apremont
canvas 32³/₈×57⁵/₈ (82.2×146.4) signed: *Th. Rousseau*
Purchased 1957
3062

Charles René Paul de SAINT-MARCEAUX 1845-1915
Study of a lioness
pen and wash 6¹/₄×11⁷/₈ (15.9×30.2) signed: *St M*
Presented by Messrs T & R Annan & Sons 1960
60-13ab

Adrien Jacques SAUZAY 1841-1928
The pond at Vaugoing *c*1882
canvas 45×78 (114.3×198.1) signed: *A. Sauzay*
Teacher Bequest 1898
843

Georges Pierre SEURAT   1859-1891
House among trees   *c*1883
wood 6¹/₈×9⁷/₈ (15.6×25.1) unsigned
McInnes Bequest 1944
2421

Georges Pierre SEURAT 1859-1891
The river banks *c*1883
wood 6¹/₄×9⁷/₈ (15.9×25.1) unsigned
McInnes Bequest 1944
2422

Georges Pierre SEURAT 1859-1891
Boy sitting on the grass *c*1882
canvas 25×31⅜ (63.5×79.6) unsigned
Presented by the Trustees of David W T Cargill 1950
2857

Paul SIGNAC 1863-1935
Coal crane, Clichy
canvas 23¼×36 (59×91.4) signed: *P. Signac/1884*
Hamilton Bequest 1946
2574

Paul SIGNAC 1863-1935
Sunset at Herblay 1889-90
canvas 22½×35½ (57.1×90.2) signed: *P. Signac 90.* inscribed: *Op. 206*
Presented by H M Government, by whom accepted in lieu of estate duty, 1976
3324

Lucien SIMON 1855-1945
Staging post *c*1913
canvas 19×24¾ (48.3×62.9) signed: *L. Simon*
McInnes Bequest 1944
2423

Lucien SIMON 1855-1945
After the war *c*1919
canvas 33½×43⅜ (85.1×110.3) signed: *L. Simon*
Presented by Marc A Béra 1948
2794

Lucien SIMON 1855-1945
Horses running free
gouache 27¼×41 (69.2×104.2) signed: *L. Simon*
Presented by Mrs Heather Napier in memory of
Mrs Vera Hedderwick 1981
81-10

Alfred SISLEY 1839-1899
Village street, Moret-sur-Loing *c*1894
canvas 15×18¹/₈ (38.1×46) signed: *Sisley*
McInnes Bequest 1944
2424

Alfred SISLEY 1839-1899
Boatyard at Saint Mammès *c*1886
canvas 15×22 (38.1×55.8) signed: *Sisley.*
Hamilton Bequest 1944
2464

Paul Constant SOYER 1823-1903
The dead bird
canvas 26½×22 (67.3×55.9) signed: *P. SOYER/1886.*
Bequeathed by John Robertson 1895
721

Constant TROYON 1810-1865
Landscape and cattle
canvas 25⅝×36⅝ (65×93.1) signed: *TROYON*
Presented by the sons of James Reid of Auchterarder 1896
735

Constant TROYON 1810-1865
Sheep
canvas 11½×20⅝ (29.2×52.4) signed in monogram: *CT55*
Donald Bequest 1905
1118

Constant TROYON 1810-1865
Returning from market
canvas 36⅛×28⅞ (91.8×73.4) signed: *C. TROYON. 1851*
Donald Bequest 1905
1145

Constant TROYON 1810-1865
Cattle
canvas 18⅛×15 (46×38.1) signed: *C. TROYON*
Donald Bequest 1905
1133

UNKNOWN, FRANCO-ITALIAN *c*1450-1475
The nativity with St Jerome, a pope and a cardinal
wood 20⅝×16⅜ (52.2×41.8) unsigned
McLellan Bequest 1854
158

UNKNOWN mid 18th century
Figures in a park
canvas 10¾×14 (27.3×35.6) signed with monogram: *DR*
McLellan Bequest 1854
246

UNKNOWN late 16th century
Portrait of a lady
wood 10½×7¾ (26.7×19.7) unsigned
McLellan Bequest 1854
152

UNKNOWN late 18th century
Leda and the swan
canvas 28×38 (71.8×97.8) unsigned
McLellan Bequest 1854
220

Maurice UTRILLO 1883-1955
Village street, Auvers-sur-Oise
canvas 23⅜×28¾ (59.4×73) signed: *Maurice Utrillo. V.*
Hamilton Bequest 1941
2217

Caroline de VALORY *c*1790 – ?
The miniature
canvas 23×19 (58.4×48.3) unsigned
McLellan Bequest 1854
216

Jean Georges VIBERT 1840-1902
Priest and harlequin
watercolour 10⅜×14⅜ (26.4×36.5) signed: *J. G. Vibert.*
Presented by Mrs Wiseman 1907
1214

Victor VINCELET 1840-1871
A bunch of flowers
canvas 8½×6¼ (21.6×15.9) unsigned
Bequeathed by Mrs Anna Walker 1948
2817

Victor VINCELET 1840-1871
A vase of flowers
canvas 21½×15½ (54.5×39.3) unsigned
Bequeathed by Archibald R Henderson 1901
940
There is now no sign of the signature *V. Vincelet '70* noted
in the 1935 and 1953 catalogues

Maurice de VLAMINCK 1876-1958
A woody river scene
canvas 18$\frac{1}{8}$×21$\frac{11}{16}$ (46×55) signed: *Vlaminck*
Purchased 1958
3086

Antoine VOLLON 1833-1900
Still-life with fruit
wood 16¾×28⅜ (42.5×72.1) signed: *A. Vollon*
Donald Bequest 1905
1109

Antoine VOLLON 1833-1900
A corner of the Louvre
wood 12½×15¾ (31.8×40) signed: *A. Vollon*
Presented by Sir John Richmond 1948
2813

Simon VOUET 1590-1649
The four seasons
canvas 55¼×51 (140.3×129.5) unsigned
McLellan Bequest 1854
218

Jean Edouard VUILLARD 1868-1940
The table
cardboard 10×13½ (25.4×34.3) signed: *E. Vuillard*
McInnes Bequest 1944
2427

Jean Edouard VUILLARD 1868-1940
The lady in green
millboard 11⅞×8⅞ (30.2×22.5) signed: *Vuillard*
McInnes Bequest 1944
2426

Jean Edouard VUILLARD 1868-1940
Interior of the drawing-room
wood 14×20¾ (35.5×52.7) signed: *E. Vuillard*
McInnes Bequest 1944
2428

Jean Edouard VUILLARD 1868-1940
Lunch in the country *c*1912
pastel 18⅞×26 (47.9×66) signed: *E. Vuillard*
McInnes Bequest 1944
2445

Jean Edouard VUILLARD 1868-1940
Mother and child *c*1899
cardboard 19⅛×22¼ (48.6×56.5) signed: *E. Vuillard*
Presented by Sir John Richmond 1948
2814

after Jean Antoine WATTEAU 1684-1721
Detachment resting
canvas 25³/₁₆×31⁵/₈ (64×80.3) unsigned
Euing Bequest 1874
392
A copy of a lost original, *Détachement faisant halte*. Several
other copies or versions exist and the subject was engraved
by Cochin.

after Jean Antoine WATTEAU 1684-1721
Recruit going to join the regiment
canvas 25³/₁₆×31⁵/₈ (64×80.3) unsigned
Euing Bequest 1874
396
A copy of a lost original, *Recrue allant joindre le régiment*.
Several copies or versions exist and the subject was
engraved by Watteau and Thomassin.

after Jean Antoine WATTEAU 1684-1721
Garden scene
canvas 14³/₄×18¹/₂ (37.4×47) unsigned
Euing Bequest 1874
410
A copy, in reverse, of *La Perspective* in the Museum of
Fine Arts, Boston

Adolphe WEISZ 1838-1914
Going to Mass
canvas 21¾×13 (55.3×33) signed: *Adolphe Weisz/1868*
Bequeathed by Miss Margaret H Garroway 1947
2604

Raymond WINTZ 1884-1956
Along the coast
canvas 62×95½ (157.5×242.6) signed: *R. Wintz*
Purchased 1938
2115

Félix François Georges Philibert ZIEM 1821-1911
Constantinople – sunset
wood 21¼×30⅛ (54×76.5) signed: *Ziem.*
Chrystal Bequest 1939
2143

Subject Index

Only the principal identified subjects are listed; still-life, genre subjects, decorative themes and unnamed portraits are not included. For landscape see separate topographical index.

Topographical Index

Unspecified landscapes are not included. Locations are in France unless otherwise stated.

Numerical Index/Concordance

This index/concordance contains every picture in the collection which is now, or was in the last three relevant catalogues published by the gallery (1967, 1953, 1935 – see below), attributed to a French artist.

The left-hand column gives the register numbers of the pictures, in chronological order of accession. The numbers for works no longer attributed to French artists are in brackets.

The second column lists, in capitals, the current attribution of every French picture (all of which are illustrated in the main part of this catalogue) and, in italics, the current attributions of all other pictures originally registered as French or published as French in the 1935, 1953 or 1967 catalogues but now attributed to other schools. The letters B, D or I after the school indicate that further details will be found in the British, Dutch or Italian catalogues (see below). The absence of these letters indicates that the present attribution has not yet been published in the Gallery's catalogues.

The third and fourth columns give the attributions in the 1967 and 1953 French catalogues respectively. Items omitted are marked ● ●.

The final column gives the attribution in the 1935 catalogue plus, in brackets, the attribution in the Gallery's picture register where that differs. Non-French attributions are again in italics and omissions from the 1935 catalogue are marked ● ●.

Catalogues referred to:
1935 Catalogue of Pictures
1953 Catalogue of French Paintings
1961 Dutch, Flemish, Netherlandish and
        German Paintings (D)
1967 French School Catalogue (vol II Illustrations)
1970 Catalogue of Italian Paintings (I)
1971 Summary Catalogue of British Oil Paintings (B)

Watercolours, drawings and pastels
Since 7 February 1953 all works in the above media have been entered in the Print Room registers, but prior to that date some (but not all) such items were included in the register of oils. As a result there are two different numbering systems for watercolours, drawings and pastels. All such French items with four figure numbers are registered with the oils and are included in the main part of this index, identified by the letter P beside the number. Works with two part numbers are those registered in the Print Room and a separate list of these is given at the end of the index.

REG NO	1985 CURRENT ATTRIBUTION	1967 FRENCH SCHOOL CATALOGUE	1953 CATALOGUE OF FRENCH PAINTINGS	1935 CATALOGUE OF PICTURES Plus, where different, register attribution
48	*after* LEMOINE	*after* LEMOYNE	● ●	*Hoet*
150	*ascr. to* DUGHET	Dughet	G. Poussin	G. Poussin
152	UNKNOWN, French late 16th century	● ●	● ●	*F. Zuccaro*
158†	UNKNOWN, Franco-Italian, *c*1450-75 (D)	● ●	● ●	*Antonello da Messina*
169	*style of* DUGHET	● ●	G. Poussin	● ● (Dughet)
175	*follower of* DUGHET	*ascr. to* Dughet	G. Poussin	G. Poussin
176	NATOIRE	Natoire	Fragonard	Fragonard (*Cagliari*)
203	MASTER OF MOULINS	Master of Moulins	Master of Moulins	Master of Moulins (*Mabuse*)
(211)	*Dutch school* (D)	● ●	A. Le Nain	A. Le Nain
(212)††	*Daret* (Flemish)	● ●	● ●	● ● (Claude)
(213)	*Anesi* (Italian – I)	● ●	C. J. Vernet	C. J. Vernet
(215)	*Dietrich* (German – D)	● ●	J. B. Pater	J. B. Pater
216	De VALORY	De Valory	De Valory	De Valory
217	*after* BOULLOGNE	● ●	Vouet	Vouet (P. de Champaigne)
218	VOUET	● ●	C. A. van Loo	C. A. van Loo
219	DUPONT	Dupont	● ●	Dupont
220	UNKNOWN, French late 18th century	● ●	A. Coypel	A. Coypel (Boucher)
(222)	*Ghisolfi* (Italian – I)	● ●	N. Poussin	N. Poussin
(223)	*Tischbein* (German – D)	● ●	● ●	Boucher
(224)	*after Heinsius* (German – D)	● ●	Greuze	Greuze (Fragonard)
225	*style of* FRAGONARD	● ●	Greuze	Greuze
(226)	*Preti* (Italian – I)	● ●	● ●	● ● (Colombien)
227	*attr. to* QUILLARD	● ●	Fragonard	Fragonard (Watteau)
246	UNKNOWN, French mid 18th century	● ●	Remond	Remond

† No 158 was attributed to the Netherlandish School in the 1961 Dutch Catalogue

†† Prior to the signature being fully deciphered, no 212 was listed as Dutch School in the 1961 catalogue

REG NO	1985 CURRENT ATTRIBUTION	1967 FRENCH SCHOOL CATALOGUE	1953 CATALOGUE OF FRENCH PAINTINGS	1935 CATALOGUE OF PICTURES Plus, where different, register attribution
(306)	*Mulier* (Flemish)	*attr. to* Dughet	● ●	● ● (N. Poussin)
392	*after* WATTEAU	*after* Watteau	Watteau	Watteau
396	*after* WATTEAU	*after* Watteau	Watteau	Watteau
410	*after* WATTEAU	● ●	Lancret	● ● (Lancret)
411	*ascr. to* LECLERC	Leclerc	● ●	*Vertangen*
(413)	*after Schenström* (Danish)	● ●	● ●	*after* J. E. H. Vernet (J. E. H. Vernet)
420	*ascr. to* LECLERC	● ●	● ●	*Vertangen*
(425)	*after Erichsen* (Danish)	● ●	L. J. F. Lagrenee	L. J. F. Lagrenée (Unknown)
433	*after* GREUZE	● ●	Greuze	Greuze
435	De GUIMARD	De Guimard	De Guimard	De Guimard
(589)	*Hennin* (Flemish)	● ●	F. Millet	F. Millet
596	DUGHET	Dughet	G. Poussin	G. Poussin
721	SOYER	Soyer	● ●	Soyer
732	COROT	Corot	Corot	Corot
735	TROYON	Troyon	Troyon	Troyon
740	JACQUE	Jacque	Jacque	Jacque
774	E. PAVY	E. Pavy	E. Pavy	E. Pavy
811	ANDRE	André	André	André
818	P. PAVY	P. Pavy	P. Pavy	P. Pavy
(822)	*De Beul* (Belgian)	De Beal	De Beal	De Beal
827	P. PAVY	P. Pavy	P. Pavy	P. Pavy
836	E. PAVY	E. Pavy	E. Pavy	E. Pavy
837	LEMMENS	Lemmens	Lemmens	Lemmens
839	P. PAVY	P. Pavy	P. Pavy	P. Pavy
843	SAUZAY	Sauzay	Sauzay	Sauzay
871	E. PAVY	E. Pavy	E. Pavy	E. Pavy
(900)	*Garzi* (Italian – I)	● ●	N. Poussin	N. Poussin
939	MONTICELLI	Monticelli	Monticelli	Monticelli
940	VINCELET	Vincelet	Vincelet	Vincelet
1017	*after* PARROCEL	● ●	J. B. van Loo	J. B. van Loo

REG NO	1985 CURRENT ATTRIBUTION	1967 FRENCH SCHOOL CATALOGUE	1953 CATALOGUE OF FRENCH PAINTINGS	1935 CATALOGUE OF PICTURES Plus, where different, register attribution
(1086)	*after Mytens* (British)	● ●	● ●	*after* Clouet (Clouet)
1109	VOLLON	Vollon	Vollon	Vollon
1111	MILLET	Millet	Millet	Millet
1112	*ascr. to* COROT	Corot	Corot	Corot
1114	DIAZ	Diaz	Diaz	Diaz
1115	COROT	Corot	Corot	Corot
1117	DIAZ	Diaz	Diaz	Diaz
1118	TROYON	Troyon	Troyon	Troyon
1119P	MILLET	Millet	Millet	Millet
1120	COROT	Corot	Corot	Corot
1122	ROUSSEAU	Rousseau	Rousseau	Rousseau
1124	ROUSSEAU	Rousseau	Rousseau	Rousseau
1129	DECAMPS	Decamps	Decamps	Decamps
1130	J. DUPRE	J. Dupré	J. Dupré	J. Dupré
1133	TROYON	Troyon	Troyon	Troyon
1134	FRERE	Frère	Frère	Frère
1135	MONTICELLI	Monticelli	Monticelli	Monticelli
1141	DAUBIGNY	Daubigny	Daubigny	Daubigny
1145	TROYON	Troyon	Troyon	Troyon
1148	*ascr. to* COROT	Corot	Corot	Corot
1157	LAMBINET	Lambinet	Lambinet	Lambinet
1159	DIAZ	Diaz	Diaz	Diaz
1160	*ascr. to* COROT	Corot	Corot	Corot
1164	DUVERGER	● ●	Duverger	Duverger
1214P	VIBERT	Vibert	Vibert	Vibert
1236	MONTICELLI	Monticelli	Monticelli	Monticelli
(1251)†	*J. Lessore* (British)	● ●	● ●	J. Lessore
1323	BASTIEN-LEPAGE	Bastien-Lepage	Bastien-Lepage	Bastien-Lepage
[1333††	● ●	● ●	Félix	Félix]
1451	*style of* PATEL	*style of* Patel	G. Poussin	G. Poussin

† In the 1935 catalogue this watercolour and others by Jules Lessore were listed as French but the artist is now generally regarded as British school

†† Despite bearing a register number, no 1333 was never a part of the Gallery's collection, being on loan from The Royal Glasgow Institute of the Fine Arts, who withdrew it, along with a number of British pictures, in 1969.

REG NO	1985 CURRENT ATTRIBUTION	1967 FRENCH SCHOOL CATALOGUE	1953 CATALOGUE OF FRENCH PAINTINGS	1935 CATALOGUE OF PICTURES Plus, where different, register attribution
1463	LEGROS	● ●	Legros	Legros
1495	HYON	Hyon	Hyon	Hyon
1529	L. V. DUPRE	L. V. Dupré	L. V. Dupré	L. V. Dupré
1536ᴾ	DUCULTIL	Ducultil	● ●	Ducultil
1561	METTLING	Mettling	Mettling	Mettling
1589	*attr. to* LACROIX	● ●	C. J. Vernet	C. J. Vernet
(1685)	*Unknown* (British – B)	● ●	● ●	Unknown, French School (?) (Clouet)
1695ᴾ	LALOUE	Laloue	Laloue	Laloue
1727†	*ascr. to* BELLANGER and *M. Maris* (D)	● ●	● ●	*M. Maris*
1795	FANTIN-LATOUR	Fantin-Latour	Fantin-Latour	Fantin-Latour
1832	HARPIGNIES	Harpignies	Harpignies	Harpignies
1873	*studio of* DELACROIX	Delacroix	Delacroix	Delacroix
2077	DUPLESSIS	Duplessis	Duplessis	all French pictures numbered from 2077 onwards were acquired after the publication of the 1935 catalogue
2083	LECOMTE	Lecomte	Lecomte	
2084	MONTEZIN	Montezin	Montezin	
2115	WINTZ	Wintz	Wintz	
2116	GRANDGERARD	Grandgerard	Grandgerard	
2117	RENI-Mel	Reni-Mel	Reni-Mel	
2135	*ascr. to* COROT	Corot	Corot	
2136	DAUBIGNY	Daubigny	Daubigny	
2137	DAUBIGNY	Daubigny	Daubigny	
2138	FANTIN-LATOUR	Fantin-Latour	Fantin-Latour	
2139	FANTIN-LATOUR	Fantin-Latour	Fantin-Latour	
2140	LHERMITTE	Lhermitte	Lhermitte	
2141	MONTICELLI	Monticelli	Monticelli	
2142	MONTICELLI	Monticelli	Monticelli	
2143	ZIEM	Ziem	Ziem	
2165ᴾ	LHERMITTE	Lhermitte	Lhermitte	

† No 1727 was published under M. Maris in the 1961 Dutch catalogue

REG NO	1985 CURRENT ATTRIBUTION	1967 FRENCH SCHOOL CATALOGUE	1953 CATALOGUE OF FRENCH PAINTINGS	1935 CATALOGUE OF PICTURES Plus, where different, register attribution
2189	METTLING	Mettling	● ●	
2193	LE SIDANER	Le Sidaner	Le Sidaner	
2197	MATISSE	Matisse	Matisse	
2200	MAZE	Maze	● ●	
2217	UTRILLO	Utrillo	Utrillo	
2229	LHERMITTE	Lhermitte	Lhermitte	
2230	imitator of DAUBIGNY	Daubigny	Daubigny	
2235P	HARPIGNIES	Harpignies	Harpignies	
2283	DERAIN	Derain	Derain	
2330	MEISSONIER	Meissonier	Meissonier	
2336	MONET	Monet	Monet	
2346	MASURE	Masure	Masure	
2348	PASCAL	Pascal	Pascal	
2375	DE BEAUMONT	De Beaumont	De Beaumont	
2376	BONNARD	Bonnard	Bonnard	
2377	BONVIN	Bonvin	Bonvin	
2378	BOUDIN	Boudin	Boudin	
2379	BOUDIN	Boudin	Boudin	
2380	BRAQUE	Braque	Braque	
2382	CEZANNE	Cézanne	Cézanne	
2383	COROT	Corot	Corot	
2384	COURBET	Courbet	Courbet	
2385	DAUMIER	Daumier	Daumier	
2386	FANTIN-LATOUR	Fantin-Latour	Fantin-Latour	
2387	FANTIN-LATOUR	Fantin-Latour	Fantin-Latour	
2389	HERVIER	Hervier	Hervier	
2400	JONGKIND	Jongkind	Jongkind	
2401	LEPINE	Lepine	Lepine	
2402	MATISSE	Matisse	Matisse	
2403	MONET	Monet	Monet	
2404	MONTICELLI	Monticelli	Monticelli	
2417	PICASSO	Picasso	Picasso	
2418	RENOIR	Renoir	Renoir	

REG NO	1985 CURRENT ATTRIBUTION	1967 FRENCH SCHOOL CATALOGUE	1953 CATALOGUE OF FRENCH PAINTINGS	1935 CATALOGUE OF PICTURES Plus, where different, register attribution
2419	RENOIR	Renoir	Renoir	
2420	RENOIR	Renoir	Renoir	
2421	SEURAT	Seurat	Seurat	
2422	SEURAT	Seurat	Seurat	
2423	SIMON	Simon	Simon	
2424	SISLEY	Sisley	Sisley	
2425	VAN GOGH	van Gogh	van Gogh	
2426	VUILLARD	Vuillard	Vuillard	
2427	VUILLARD	Vuillard	Vuillard	
2428	VUILLARD	Vuillard	Vuillard	
2435^P	JONGKIND	Jongkind	Jongkind	
2441^P	DEGAS	Degas	Degas	
2445^P	VUILLARD	Vuillard	Vuillard	
(2452)	*studio of Desmarées* (Swedish)	● ●	Largillière	
2464	SISLEY	Sisley	Sisley	
2465	GAUGUIN	Gauguin	Gauguin	
2553	PASCAL	Pascal	Pascal	
2574	SIGNAC	Signac	Signac	
2599^P	DETAILLE	Detaille	Detaille	
2600	L. GERARD	L. Gerard	L. Gerard	
2601	GROLLERON	Grolleron	Grolleron	
2602	KRATKE	Kratké	Kratké	
2604	WEISZ	Weisz	● ●	
2632	BILLET	Billet	Billet	
2690^P	LHERMITTE	Lhermitte	Lhermitte	
2692	*follower of* FRAGONARD	M. Gerard	M. Gerard	
2693	*follower of* FRAGONARD	M. Gerard	M. Gerard	
2694	*follower of* FRAGONARD	M. Gerard	M. Gerard	
[2695†	● ●	● ●	M. Gerard]	
2775	*ascr. to* COURBET	Courbet	Courbet	

† No 2695 was stolen from the gallery in 1963 and has never been recovered

REG NO	1985 CURRENT ATTRIBUTION	1967 FRENCH SCHOOL CATALOGUE	1953 CATALOGUE OF FRENCH PAINTINGS	1935 CATALOGUE OF PICTURES Plus, where different, register attribution
2794	SIMON	Simon	Simon	
2811	PISSARRO	Pissarro	Pissarro	
2812ᴾ	LE SIDANER	Le Sidaner	Le Sidaner	
2813	VOLLON	Vollon	Vollon	
2814	VUILLARD	Vuillard	Vuillard	
2817	VINCELET	Vincelet	Vincelet	
2825	MICHONZE	Michonze	● ●	
2853	BONVIN	Bonvin	Bonvin	
2857	SEURAT	Seurat	Seurat	
2858	COROT	Corot	Corot	
2859	COURBET	Courbet	Courbet	
2897	GUILLAUMIN	Guillaumin	Guillaumin	
2902	MARCOUSSIS	Marcoussis	Marcoussis	
2909	GUILLAUMIN	Guillaumin	Guillaumin	
2916	BOUDIN	Boudin	Boudin	
2917	FANTIN-LATOUR	Fantin-Latour	Fantin-Latour	
2930	LHOTE	Lhote	Lhote	
2931	LHOTE	Lhote	Lhote	
2932	CEZANNE	Cézanne	Cézanne	
2933	FANTIN-LATOUR	Fantin-Latour	Fantin-Latour	
2934	PISSARRO	Pissarro	Pissarro	
2958	*after* BOUCHER	*after* Boucher	*school of* Boucher	
2959	*after* BOUCHER	*after* Boucher	*school of* Boucher	
2980	CASSATT	Cassatt	Cassatt	
2999†	*after* LEMOINE	● ●	all French pictures numbered from 2999 onwards were acquired after the publication of the 1953 catalogue	
3030	MARQUET	Marquet		
3062	ROUSSEAU	Rousseau		
3063	CAMOIN	Camoin		
3086	VLAMINCK	Vlaminck		
3101	ROUAULT	Rouault		

† Purchased with an attribution to Gavin Hamilton (British 1723-1798; see 1971 catalogue)

REG NO	1985 **CURRENT ATTRIBUTION**	1967 **FRENCH SCHOOL CATALOGUE**	1953 **CATALOGUE OF FRENCH PAINTINGS**	1935 **CATALOGUE OF PICTURES** Plus, where different, register attribution
3110	FRIESZ	Friesz		
3111	MICHEL	Michel		
3120	DUFY	Dufy		
3126	DAGNAN- BOUVERET	Dagnan-Bouveret		
3132	JULLIOTTE	Julliott		
3150†	*attr. to* BLANCHET	● ●		
3168	MORET	Moret		
3315	VAN GOGH	all French pictures numbered from 3315 onwards were acquired after the publication of the 1967 catalogue		
3318	LUCE			
3324	SIGNAC			
3329	GRIS			
3352	DORE			
3396	BRETON			
3401	BERNARD			

Watercolours, Drawings and Pastels listed in the Print Room registers – see notes at start of index

REG NO	1985	1967	1953	1935
24-4	LEGROS	Legros	● ●	● ●
24-4a	LEGROS	Legros	● ●	● ●
25-26gk	HARPIGNIES	Harpignies	● ●	● ●
53-3	LEGROS	Legros	all items numbered from 53-3 onwards were acquired after the publication of the 1935 and 1953 catalogues	
53-3a	LEGROS	Legros		
60-13ab	SAINT-MARCEAUX	● ●		
62-3	HARPIGNIES	Harpignies		
64-3	JACQUE	Jacque		
81-10	SIMON	acquired after 1967		
U.29	GAVARNI	Gavarni		
U.30	*ascr. to* COURTOIS	● ●		

† Purchased with an attribution to Allan Ramsay (British 1713-1784; not published)